Kiboko
and the water snake

Written by Frances Usher

Illustrated by Stephen Lewis

Heinemann

In Africa there was a beautiful river.
By the river were tall trees
and lots of green grass.
In the river lived a little hippopotamus
called Kiboko.

2

One day Kiboko and his mother
were sitting by the river.
Kiboko was very hot.
'Why don't you get down under the water?'
said his mother.

So Kiboko went down under the
cold water.
'Mmmm, that's good,' he said.
Just then someone called out from
under the water, 'Help! Help!
Take your big foot off me!'

Kiboko looked down into the water
but he could not see his feet.
All he could see was lots and lots of mud.
'Who is down there?' he called.
'I can't see who you are.'

Then Kiboko saw something
swimming up out of the water.

It was a little green water snake and
she said, 'I was doing my snake dance
when you put your big foot on me.'

'I'm sorry if I hurt you,' said Kiboko.
'I just didn't see you down there. But
I would like to see your snake dance.
Will you show me?'

'It's like this,' said the little green
water snake and she began to dance
very fast for Kiboko. She went
this way and that way, over him and
under him.

'That is a beautiful dance,' said
Kiboko. 'I'm going to dance like
that too.'
And Kiboko began to dance.

Kiboko danced this way and that way.

Up and down.

Hop, hop.

Jump, jump.

He danced off down
the river. But he didn't
see the crocodiles on
the other bank of
the river.

The crocodiles began to swim after
Kiboko.

'Look out, Kiboko!' called the little
snake. 'The crocodiles are after you.'
But Kiboko didn't hear the snake
calling. He just went on dancing.

The crocodiles swam up to Kiboko.
He saw their big tails, their big mouths
and their big teeth. He called out,
'Help! Help! The crocodiles are going
to eat me.'

Kiboko's mother could hear Kiboko
calling out. She jumped into the water
and swam over to him as fast as
she could. Just as the crocodiles opened
their big mouths to eat Kiboko,
she pushed him out of their way.

Kiboko and his mother swam back
across the river and climbed up
on to the bank.

'Kiboko,' said his mother, 'you **must**
look out for crocodiles. They like
to eat little hippos like you.'

When the crocodiles had gone, Kiboko
went back into the water. He saw the
little green water snake doing her dance.
'Are you going to dance again, Kiboko?'
asked the snake.
'Yes,' said Kiboko. 'But not today.
I think I'll just look out for crocodiles.'